Jan Depreter

Northern Lights

compositions for guitar solo

Sy. 2887

RICORDI

In den letzten zehn Jahren habe ich oft über die Länder gestaunt, die ich besuchte. Als kleiner Junge, der Gitarre lernte, hätte ich mir nie träumen lassen, dass diese kleine Wunderkiste mich einst um die Welt und zurück bringen würde, bevor ich 30 wäre. Die Stücke in den beiden Bänden „Wit" und „Northern Lights" sind Schnappschüsse von mich tief berührenden Augenblicken, inspirierenden Orten und Personen, die ich unterwegs getroffen und in manchen Fällen wieder verloren habe.

Der 2011 veröffentlichte Band „Wit" beinhaltet die technisch etwas weniger fordernden Stücke und eignet sich für Gitarristen ab der Mittelstufe.
Das vorliegende Album, „Northern Lights", stellt Fortgeschrittene vor lohnende Aufgaben.

In the past decennium I have often marvelled at the countries I have visited. As a boy learning the guitar, I never could have dreamed that this little wooden box of wonders would take me around the globe and back again before the age of 30. The pieces presented in these two volumes, "Wit" and "Northern Lights", are snapshots of deeply emotional moments and inspiring places and persons I have met, and sometimes lost again, along the way.

The first instalment "Wit", published in 2011, features the technically somewhat less demanding pieces, fit for all guitar students from intermediate level onwards, while this second album "Northern Lights" presents a rewarding challenge to all advanced players.

Jan Depreter

to David Russell

The Isle of Skye

Jan Depreter
(*1975)

Edition Ricordi

Sy. 2887

to Marleen Van Loo

Northern Lights

(Tremolo Study)

Jan Depreter
(*1975)

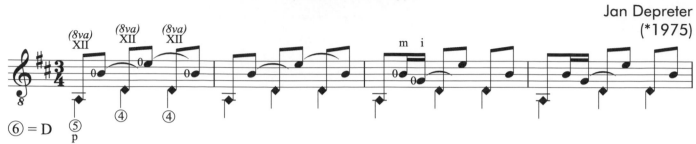

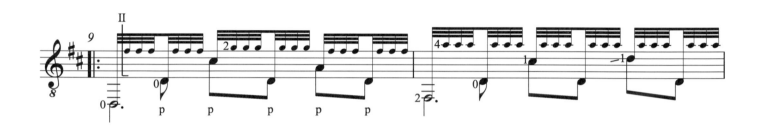

1) Bei der Wiederholung B statt d1 spielen.
1) Second time play B♭ instead of d1.

Edition Ricordi   Sy. 2887   © 2013 by G. Ricordi & Co.

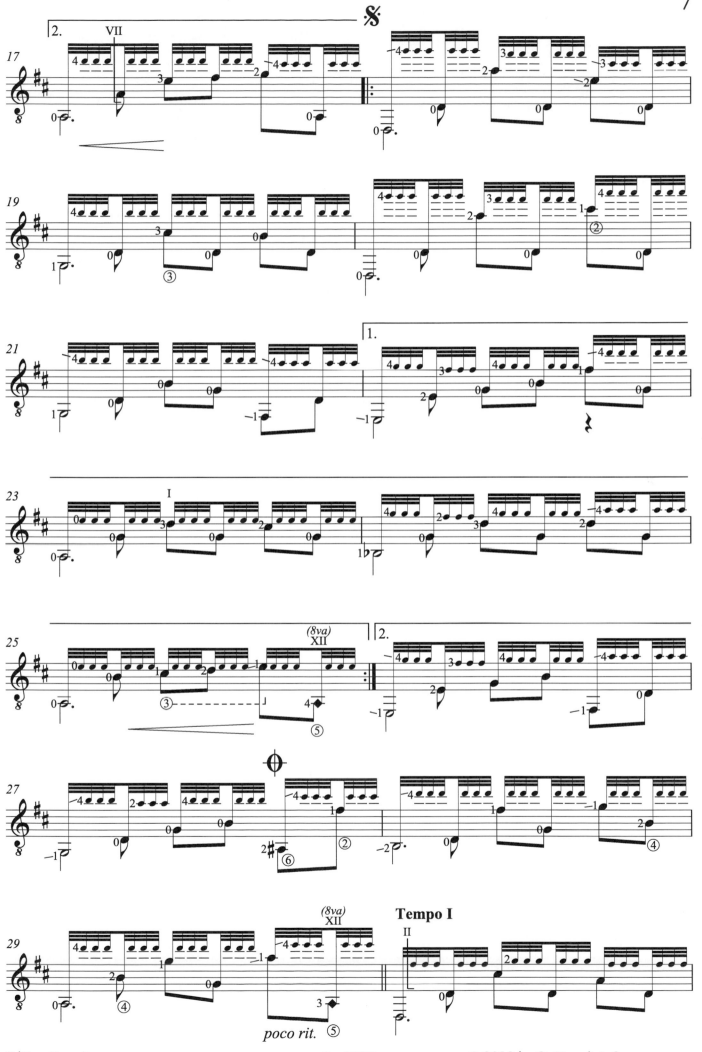

Sy. 2887

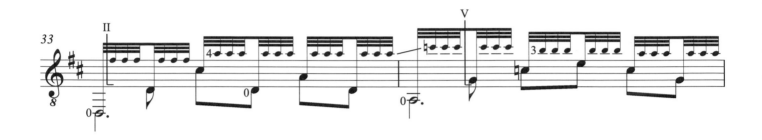

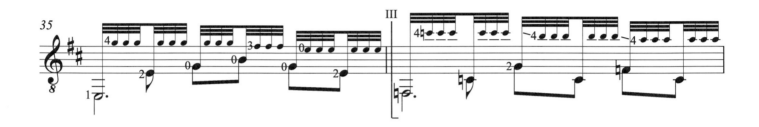

poco a poco cresc.

D. S. al

con rip.

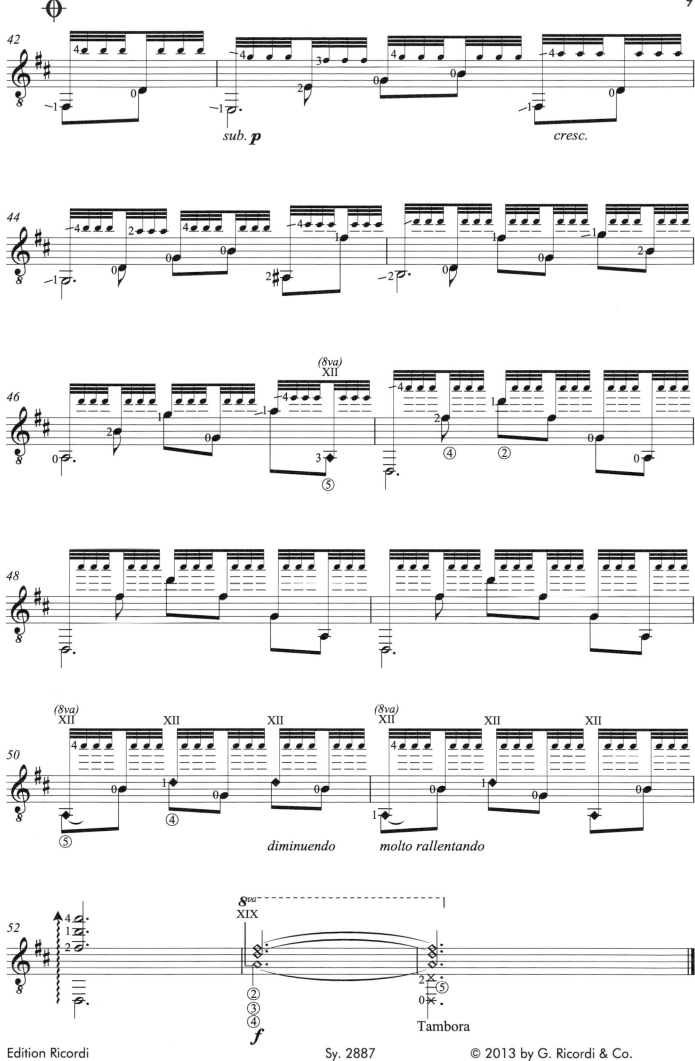

to Cang Guan

Vals Venezolano Nº 2

(Isabelle)

Jan Depreter
(*1975)

1), 2) Anmerkungen siehe S. 24 / *see p. 24 for Annotations*

Edition Ricordi   Sy. 2887   © 2013 by G. Ricordi & Co.

3), 4) Anmerkungen siehe S. 24 / *see p. 24 for Annotations*

Edition Ricordi   Sy. 2887   © 2013 by G. Ricordi & Co.

12

5), 6) Anmerkungen siehe S. 24 / see p. 24 for Annotations

Sy. 2887

to Zoran Dukic

Vals Venezolano N° 3

Jan Depreter
(*1975)

1) <u>Alle</u> Flageoletts in diesem Stück mit der rechten Hand ausführen
1) Produce <u>all</u> harmonics in this piece with the right hand.

ritenuto

Edition Ricordi   Sy. 2887   © 2013 by G. Ricordi & Co.

Sy. 2887

to my parents, Marc and Rita

Moreliana

Homage to Sergei Rachmaninov (1873–1943)

Jan Depreter
(*1975)

Sy. 2887 © 2013 by G. Ricordi & Co.

Sy. 2887 © 2013 by G. Ricordi & Co.

Sy. 2887

1) 4 greift auf der 1. Saite am 10. Bund, i berührt die 1. Saite am 17. Bund, a schlägt 1. Saite an.
1) Left hand 4th finger takes the 1st string on fret X while right hand finger i softly touches the same string at fret XVII and finger a strikes it.

Edition Ricordi   Sy. 2887

Hikari

Light

Jan Depreter
(*1975)

⑥ = D

tasto

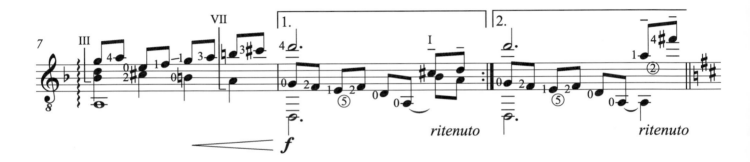

ritenuto   ritenuto

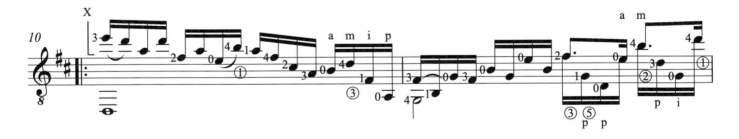

Edition Ricordi Sy. 2887

Edition Ricordi

Sy. 2887

Anmerkungen zu *Vals Venezolano N° 2*

1) (Takt 15) Barréfinger zu den Basssaiten hin aufklappen, Druck auf die 1. Saite bestehen lassen, hörbar zwei bis drei Lagen nach oben gleiten. Danach schlägt der 4. Finger (linke Hand) auf die 1. Saite, es erklingt h¹ (Glissando mit abschließender Aufwärtsbindung).

2) (Takt 30) Hörbares Gleiten mit dem 4. Finger auf der 1. Saite. Der Endton wird angeschlagen (Portamento)

3) (Takt 51) Gedämpfter Klang durch Auflegen des Barréfingers <u>auf</u> dem Bundstab

4) (Takt 53) Glissando ohne Endton

5) (Takt 71) Der 4. Finger führt vom lediglich gegriffenen (nicht angeschlagenen!) d¹ ein kräftiges Glissando zum fis¹ aus.

6) (Takt 80ff.) Gedämpfter Klang durch loses Auflegen des Greiffingers im Bereich des Bundfelds

Annotations for *Vals Venezolano N° 2*

1) (bar 15) Lift the barré finger slightly towards the bass strings, keep the pressure on the first string; slide upwards two or three frets. After this slide, the fourth finger (left hand) taps on the first string producing a b¹ (glissando terminating in an upward slur).

2) (bar 30) The fourth finger slides audibly on the first string. Attack the final note as usual (portamento).

3) (bar 51) Produce a muted sound by putting the barré finger exactly <u>on</u> the fret ridge.

4) (bar 53) Glissando without a definite final note

5) (bar 71) The fourth finger carries out a strong glissando from d¹, which is only fingered (not attacked!), to f#¹.

6) (bar 80ff.) Produce a muted sound by putting the finger only loosely on its position between the frets.